GLOBAL ECONOMICS
AND THE ENVIRONMENT

GLOBAL ECONOMICS AND THE ENVIRONMENT

Toward Sustainable Rural Development in the Third World

ROGER D. STONE
EVE HAMILTON

COUNCIL ON FOREIGN RELATIONS PRESS
NEW YORK

COUNCIL ON FOREIGN RELATIONS BOOKS

The Council on Foreign Relations, Inc., is a nonprofit and nonpartisan organization devoted to promoting improved understanding of international affairs through the free exchange of ideas. The Council does not take any position on questions of foreign policy and has no affiliation with, and receives no funding from, the United States government.

From time to time, books and monographs written by members of the Council's research staff or visiting fellows, or commissioned by the Council, or written by an independent author with critical review contributed by a Council study or working group are published with the designation "Council on Foreign Relations Book." Any book or monograph bearing that designation is, in the judgment of the Committee on Studies of the Council's Board of Directors, a responsible treatment of a significant international topic worthy of presentation to the public. All statements of fact and expressions of opinion contained in Council books are, however, the sole responsibility of the author.

Library of Congress Cataloguing-in-Publication Data

Stone, Roger D.
    Global economics and the environment : toward sustainable rural development in the Third World / by Roger Stone and Eve Hamilton.
    p. cm.
    Includes bibliographical references.
    ISBN 0-87609-108-7
    1. Environmental policy—Developing countries. 2. Rural development—Environmental aspects—Developing countries.
    I. Hamilton, Eve, 1967–   . II. Title
    HC59.72.E5S75 1991
    363.7'056'091724--dc20

91–25511
CIP

91   92   93   94   95   96   PB   10   9   8   7   6   5   4   3   2   1
Cover Design: Whit Vye

Contents

Foreword

The world over, many individuals and institutions perceive tightening symmetry between those battle-weary enemies, economics and the environment. Now as ever, goals for material wealth need on occasion to be modified for the sake of the environment. Economic imperatives will sometimes require environmental compromises. Still, in view of accumulating evidence documenting the coincidence of economic and environmental success—or failure—many observers see a closer overall relationship taking shape between the two development poles.

Nowhere does this greater harmony offer more promise than in the rural tropics of the Third World, where much of the global quest for a sustainable future will be won or lost. Over the longer term, efforts to increase the economic return from these species-rich areas of mangrove and reef, towering forest and broad floodplain will tend to succeed if environmental quality is maintained. At the same time, if these areas advance economically, hundreds of millions of poor people occupying them will become able to survive without continuing to degrade the ecosystems of which they are part.

Recognizing these realities, tropical villagers in many developing countries have begun to seek environmentally sound solutions to their economic problems. But if their cumulative efforts are to result in the broad achievement of concurrent economic and environmental progress in the rural Third World, national leaders in both the South and the North will have to work hard to lower long-standing institutional barriers that obstruct the path to success. Comprehensive policy changes will have to take place in the capitals of developing countries, many of whose governments have paid scant attention to the needs of the rural sector. Adjustments in the trade, financial, and investment policies of advanced nations would also do much to facilitate the achievement of sustainability in the Third World's rural byways.

The World Commission on Environment and Development—the high-level panel convened by the United Nations in 1983, and chaired by Norwegian Prime Minister Gro Harlem Brundtland—explored many of these issues during its deliberations. *Our Common Future,* the Commission's widely distributed report, underscored them, and they have been under frequent discussion since its publication in 1987. Surely they will be a central topic at the upcoming Earth Summit—the United Nations Conference on Environment and Development (UNCED), scheduled to be held in Rio de Janeiro in June 1992.

In the meantime, in January 1991, the Council on Foreign Relations and the World Resources Institute jointly convened a multidisciplinary panel of experts to address the particular question of what steps advanced nations might take to facilitate progress toward sustainable development in the rural tropics. This report summarizes the findings of this colloquium, which took place at the Council's headquarters in New York City. Following a brief introduction, the reader will find participants' general views on the links between Northern policies and their consequences in the rural Third World. These are divided into four sections: debt, trade, public investment, and private investment. Each section contains certain participants' specific recommendations. As preparations for UNCED proceed apace, we hope that many of these suggestions will receive careful consideration. A set of more general observations regarding the UNCED exercise as a whole and a list of those who attended the January colloquium follow these recommendations. Responsibility for the views expressed in this report, we must emphasize, rests only with its coauthors.

Finally, the organizers would like to express their heartfelt thanks to those institutions that provided the financial support required to carry out the colloquium's activities. The project received special grants from Citicorp, the John D. and Catherine T. MacArthur Foundation, the Marpat Foundation, and (via its support for the World Resources Institute's Center for International Development and Environment) the U.S. Agency for International Development.

Peter Tarnoff
President
Council on Foreign Relations

James Gustave Speth
President
World Resources Institute

GLOBAL ECONOMICS AND THE ENVIRONMENT

INTRODUCTION

Despite accelerating urbanization throughout what are known as developing countries, much of their poverty remains a rural affair. Four-fifths of Sub-Saharan Africa's poorest, well over half of those in Asia, and almost half of the most needy in Latin America and the Caribbean inhabit often infertile rural terrain. The number of the rural Third World's poor may increase, from about 750 million at present to about 1.25 billion, before its total population levels off in about 2015 and urban growth takes over.[1] (See Figure 1.)

Rural poverty in developing countries reaches its deepest levels in the tropics. In these same regions are also concentrated almost all the world's diversity of plant and animal life, and most of the wild germ plasm that—despite biotechnology's impressive progress—continues to have great importance for human health and well-being. Tropical forests, which occupy 6 percent of the earth's surface, are home to more than 200 million people—and perhaps 90 percent of all nonhuman species. As many as one-half of all kinds of plants and animals may be restricted to only 2 percent of the planet, almost all of it in the tropical zone.

Much environmental degradation is a consequence of affluence. But what many poor people of the rural tropics must do to survive also severely damages the ecosystems of which they form a part. Compelled to disregard longer-

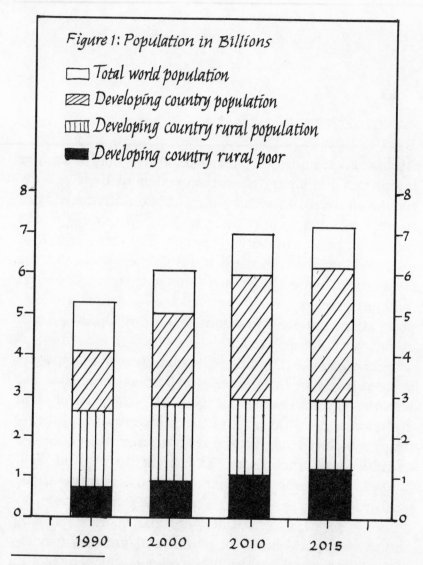

Figure 1: Population in Billions

☐ Total world population
▨ Developing country population
⊞ Developing country rural population
■ Developing country rural poor

Note: Projections for present and future numbers of Third World rural *poor* derived by authors from sources.

Sources: United Nations Development Programme, *Human Development Report 1990*(New York: Oxford University Press, 1990); United Nations Systems Estimates & Projections (Pers. Comm.); H. Jeffrey Leonard, ed., *Environment and the Poor: Development Strategies for a Common Agenda* (Washington, D.C.: Overseas Development Council, 1989); Robert Repetto, "Population, Resources, and Environment," Population Bulletin, Vol. 42, no. 2 (1987).

term consequences, they cut ever deeper into forests to create farms and pastures, and overharvest available natural resources along coasts and in other regions of particular biological importance. Their actions have been an important factor in bringing about extinction rates of plant and animal species that are higher than any the world has experienced since dinosaurs disappeared 65 million years ago. By 2015, one-quarter of all species present on the planet in the mid-1980s may have vanished.[2] This loss, the biologist Edward O. Wilson of Harvard University has stressed, is the sin for which current generations can least be forgiven.[3]

Over the past decade, conservationists and aid donors have learned much about how to introduce "sustainable" forms of development in the rural tropics.[4] Properly applied, new technologies and agricultural innovations can do much to alleviate a large share of the world's deepest poverty while also protecting the integrity of fragile ecosystems and the biological diversity within them. Greater attention to the needs of the Third World's rural poor will also slow the rate of their migration to already teeming urban areas. A new emphasis on this sector of human development, therefore, has multiple advantages.

In the opinion of many observers, achieving rural sustainability in developing countries requires an unprecedented burst of economic growth. Overall, according to Jim MacNeill, the environmentalist who served as secretary-general of the World Commission on Environment and Development—the high-level panel convened by the United Nations in 1983 and chaired by Norwegian Prime Minister Gro Harlem Brundtland (the Brundtland Commission)—a fivefold-to-tenfold increase in economic activity is "required over the next 50 years in order to meet the needs and aspirations of a burgeoning world population, as well as to begin to reduce mass poverty."[5] Others feel that it is not possible to achieve such rapid growth without provoking a breakdown in the earth's basic ability to support life. Dismissing the vision of sustainable growth as a "bad oxymoron," economist Herman Daly of the World Bank envisions an era of "sustainable development" during which the world would mount "a serious attack on poverty." Central to any such effort would be population control, income redistribution, and other measures that would not cause an increase in overall economic activity.[6]

Daly's views notwithstanding, it will become clear in subsequent sections of this report that many other analysts believe that sustainability is achievable in the context of growth. Whatever one chooses to believe about this complex issue, it is unquestionable that tropical villagers alone can do little to carry the day. Progress toward sustainability will also require major adjustments by the governments of developing countries—and throughout the community of developed nations.

In the nations of the South, governments will need to make fundamental political, economic, and cultural changes. Sharing power with the grass roots, a concession that will not come easily to many rulers in developing countries, is mandatory if environmental needs are to be efficiently addressed. More specifically, many such nations will have to take the following steps:

- Curb their appetites for military spending in favor of allocations for social progress.

- Overcome their long-standing tendency in planning fiscal and development programs to subsidize city dwellers, for political and security reasons, at the expense of the rural poor. Instead of reducing the risk of food riots by pegging such staples as milk and bread at artificially low prices, and taxing agricultural exports to a degree that only the few large-scale farmers can tolerate, they will need to place greater emphasis on broadly accessible, environmentally and economically sound forms of rural development.

- Make revisions in traditional land-tenure patterns to bring about increases in production on good land and lessen the pressures on marginal or virgin areas that stem from widespread landlessness.

- Pay more serious attention to the population question.

- Improve levying and collecting of taxes. The World Bank has calculated that it would take no more than a 2 percent tax on the incomes of the Latin American and Caribbean region's top 20 percent to raise all people there above the poverty line.[7]

Even if developing countries manage to bring about such major internal structural adjustments, their progress toward sustainability is hardly certain. Without appropriate care, economic progress within them could merely provoke new forms of environmental degradation to replace those associated with deep poverty. The experience of the 1980s, particularly in Brazil, demonstrates that attaching precise environmental conditionalities to development loans does not assure compliance. Nevertheless, since it *is* guaranteed that little environmental *or* economic advancement will occur *without* the North's help, the direct interface between global economic practices and the prospects for sustainability in the rural tropics warrants close scrutiny.

The North can participate not only by increasing aid flows, but also by modifying a number of economic practices that have helped keep the South poor. Creative, even radical new steps will be needed to accomplish the following:

- Reverse the net flow of capital from poor to rich countries, which now amounts to $50 billion or more per year.

- Reorder international trade to benefit poor nations.

- Stimulate environmentally sound private investments in the South.

- Make the technologies needed for sustainable development available on affordable terms.

- Increase bilateral and multilateral financial aid for Third World development.

This report stresses these themes, which formed the heart of a two-day colloquium that the Council on Foreign Relations and the World Resources Institute jointly held in January 1991.

DEBT

Third World debt, already a mounting problem during the 1970s, became a veritable crisis during the 1980s as the figures continued their rapid climb. In 1991 the face value of outstanding debt surpassed $1.3 trillion. Annual total debt service due amounted to nearly $200 billion—quadruple the sum that the Organization for Economic Coop-

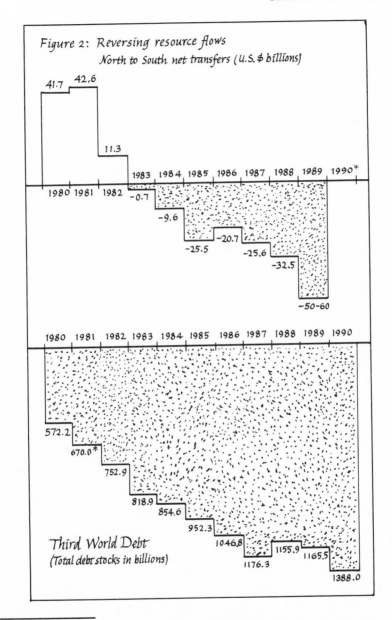

Figure 2: Reversing resource flows
North to South net transfers (U.S. $ billions)

Third World Debt
(Total debt stocks in billions)

Note: Figure for net resources in 1990 not available; figure for 1981 Third World
debt taken from *World Debt Tables 1987–88*

Sources: United Nations Development Programme, *Human Development Report
1990* (New York: Oxford University Press, 1990), p. 79; World Bank,
World Debt Tables 1989–90, External Debt of Developing Countries,
Volume I (Washington, D.C.: World Bank, 1989), p. 78.

eration and Development (OECD) spends each year on multilateral and bilateral development assistance.[8] (See Figure 2.)

The direct pressures of debt service, as well as a more general crisis of confidence among investors, has resulted in an even larger problem: the reversal in the direction of overall North-South capital flows. In 1981, $42.6 billion net moved from North to South.[9] The following year Mexico defaulted on its debt, and the reverse flow, which former West German Chancellor Willy Brandt has called "a blood transfusion from the sick to the healthy," began.[10] A net of about $50 billion currently moves in this "wrong" direction, much of it from the countries least able to pay. Each year Latin America alone sends elsewhere, in total, more than it spends on education.[11] Colloquium participants dwelled on the consequences of the debt and capital flow situations. "Under such conditions," asked Alvaro Umaña Quesada of Costa Rica, "how can we expect to have development of any sort?"

Since the advent of the Reagan administration's Baker Plan, which emphasized additional lending to developing countries to enable them to "grow out of debt," various mechanisms to provide direct relief have also taken shape. Although countries receiving World Bank assistance must pay their debts if they wish to receive further loans, structural adjustment programs worked out between the Bank, the International Monetary Fund (IMF), and debtor nations are designed to enable recipients to avoid defaults by means of export-led growth. Under the Bush administration's Brady Plan, and the new policies introduced by other industrial nations (including France and Canada), some official country-to-country loans have been fully forgiven. Some countries—such as Costa Rica, for example—have made sacrifices elsewhere in order to re-purchase their official debt. In the commercial sector a lively secondary market, in which debt can be traded for as little as ten cents per dollar of face value, has provided considerable relief. So have debt-for-equity arrangements, in which banks have converted debt into ownership of local enterprises in debtor nations.

Quietly negotiated in finance ministries and board-rooms, these sorts of measures have usually given little heed to environmental consequences. While any form of debt relief gives developing countries elbow room to address environmental problems if they wish to, in most instances they have no obligation to do so. Sometimes, in fact, an acceleration of environmental degradation has occurred in rural areas where the emphasis that adjustment assistance places on exports often translates very directly into larger harvests of trees from already depleted forests, more intensive cultivation in marginal areas, or speedier extraction of unrenewable minerals and oil. The need to export increases pressures on developing countries to farm lands that would be better left untouched to protect watersheds or prevent erosion, and to use environmentally unsound agricultural chemicals that have negative effects both ashore and on important marine environments in the coastal zone. Cuts in government spending, another structural adjustment staple, inhibit the capabilities of environmental management agencies. For want of funds, many national parks meant to protect biological diversity lack proper management and are overrun by poachers, squatters, miners, and other intruders.

Nigeria provides a textbook example of how structural adjustment can lead to environmental instability. There, when oil revenues collapsed in 1986, a sharp currency devaluation provided strong incentives for agricultural exports and, according to the World Bank, had the positive effect of reversing "the strong urban bias that had developed during the oil boom."[12] But thanks to what the Bank termed the revitalization of the tree crop sector, Nigeria's annual deforestation rate also became the world's second highest, far surpassing sustainable limits and heralding no more than vestigial forest cover by the year 2000. Ironically, by the late 1980s, when Nigeria had become a net *importer* of timber products, the nation was also making plans to prepare a Tropical Forestry Action Plan as part of a worldwide program to make tropical forestry sustainable.

In other countries the pressure to export brings environmentally negative consequences even more swiftly. Thus, in part because it was compelled to shift from wheat to cotton for the export market, Sudan faces a severe grain shortage and a national food crisis. The difficulties often result from lack of preparedness. In Sub-Saharan Africa, reports the World Bank, dependence on the export of primary products will be prolonged not only to meet adjustment-assistance targets, but also because weak infrastructures and lack of management capabilities inhibit the countries' ability to develop alternative export programs.[13]

Although developing countries express little fondness for environmental conditionalities, direct linkages increase the likelihood that debt reduction programs will pack an environmental punch. The pioneer idea of this sort is the so-called debt-for-nature swap, in which conservation agencies raise funds to purchase a portion of a country's commercial debt at a discount, or persuade the bank holding the debt to donate some of it. They then exchange the debt for a commitment from the debtor government to use local currency or bonds to achieve local conservation objectives. In 1987 Conservation International, a private organization, completed the first such swap with Bolivia. By January 1991 conservation agencies had paid $16.7 million to purchase debt with a face value of almost $98 million, according to the World Wildlife Fund. While these sums do not seem impressive relative to the massive total Third World debt, the more than $60 million in local conservation bonds that the swaps generated is a substantial figure in the low-budget world of environmental protection.

At the colloquium Alvaro Umaña highlighted several important advantages of the debt-for-nature concept. In Costa Rica, he stated, $40 million in swaps has attracted additional resources from donor nations; added weight to environmental goals in national planning; and encouraged long-term stability, since only the interest on the long-term bonds is spent. In one swap an investment of $5 million bought $33 million in debt. Consequently, $10 million in local resources went into a revolving fund to help small farmers embark on commercial forestry projects and to create among the farmers what Umaña called a culture of planting.

Yet even in Costa Rica, the world's most enthusiastic debt-for-nature advocate, the swaps represent only a small portion of the overall debt reduction program—from $4 billion to $3 billion in face value—that consists largely of direct government repurchases. Officials in other countries considering debt-for-nature deals have expressed apprehension both about the inflationary potential of this approach and about the loss of sovereignty that may be at risk in working directly with private international conservation groups. Although swap arrangements can be fine-tuned to circumvent such obstacles, these concerns help to explain why the debt-for-nature principle can be stretched only so far. Those seeking to link the environment to major increments of debt relief will want to develop different mechanisms involving public- as well as private-sector debt.

Several such ventures are already under way. At the regional level, the U.S. Enterprise for the Americas Initiative, launched in 1990, provides for the forgiving or "restructuring" of some official U.S. debt in return for environmental commitments from debtor nations in the Western Hemisphere. Though only a small portion of Latin America's approximately $12 billion in debt to the U.S. government was negotiable under the initial legislation, which limited the field to some concessional loans under the Public Law 480 food assistance program, the Bush administration anticipates wider applicability. Eventually, loans through the U.S. Agency for International Development (USAID), the Export-Import Bank of the United States, and the Commodity Credit Corporation may all qualify if debtor countries adhere to stringent Enterprise for the Americas conditionalities.

Among multilateral donors, the Inter-American Development Bank has begun to make loans for purchases of commercial debt, provided that the local funds generated go to environmental purposes. The World Bank, which has a policy against renegotiating its loans, is also considering a scheme whereby debtor countries could use Bank resources to buy commercial debt that is not their own. In exchange, developing countries would once again allocate local funds to environmentally sound development projects. Among scores of debt reducing proposals is the suggestion

that the World Bank and IMF act as "bankruptcy judges,"
passing binding rulings on the maximum proportion of a
country's total debt that it would have to service before
receiving special assistance.

Fiscal and political constraints, as well as the debt
burden, inhibit developing countries' ability to tackle environmental problems. In the absence of growth, Alvaro
Umaña suggested at the colloquium, interest in the environment would drop sharply. Despite the economic factors that bear on the question of environmental stability,
colloquium participants reiterated the central role that
debt plays. Among their suggestions for new initiatives
were these:

- Broaden the principle of debt-for-nature swaps to
  encompass local support for all the measures—training and institution-building, for example—that can
  benefit the environment. Include technical assistance
  as well as money in what might be called debt-for-
  environment swaps. Such linkages are important if
  debt relief is to result in environmental gains; simple
  forgiveness could be environmentally negative.

- Earmark the targeted support to empower nongovernmental agencies rather than government institutions.
  A danger of projects such as the Enterprise for the
  Americas Initiative is that, once assured of this form of
  funding for the environment, a recipient country might
  reduce its own budget by an equivalent amount. Nevertheless, colloquium participants stressed, direct assistance for governments should not be ruled out.

- Establish direct links between debt and biological
  reserves as a means of preserving biological diversity.
  The world community could forgive part or all of a

country's debt and earmark this relief directly for the maintenance of a specific site. Annual reviews of the condition of the site would lead to further debt reduction or—if the reserve had not been well protected—to the program's suspension or termination.

- Require repayment of only that portion of developing country debt deemed serviceable; thus, the remainder could be invested in development efforts. Both the world economy and the environment would thereby benefit. Outright nonpayment of debt does not represent a permanent solution.

TRADE

During the colonial era rich nations tended to regard the periphery as a dependable, low-cost supplier of primary products: rubber, coffee, cacao, timber. The negative environmental effects of their trade practices aroused little concern. After independence many developing countries, denied market access for labor-intensive manufactured goods but scrambling ever harder to avoid deepening debt problems, were forced back to the farm and forest-products sectors to generate export earnings. In their zeal to maximize such income in the context of increasingly unfavorable terms of trade, they still often adopt rural development strategies that cause grave environmental problems.

Livestock production provides an example. By 1983 Costa Rica, primarily to create pastures that would make it the world's top exporter of beef to the United States, had removed all but 17 percent of its original forest cover; when U.S. tastes changed and demand for the product diminished, Costa Rica was left with denuded land and depleted soil. European Community (EC) hunger for lean grass-fed beef also resulted in a rapid expansion of cattle raising in Botswana. Environmentalists, though not all others, view the resulting reduction of that country's once vast wildebeeste population to only one-tenth of its former size as an ecological tragedy.

Developing countries' legacy of dependence on single export crops, such as cotton or bananas, which are often planted high on hillsides that should be left in forest cover to protect watersheds, further constrains their ability to escape from trade-related environmental pitfalls. To stimulate production of bananas and other monocultures, governments often subsidize hazardous agricultural chemicals that in themselves are environmentally harmful and are often liberally applied. Usually, moreover, these products end up in the hands of larger or more favored farmers, pushing the deprived marginal population toward unsustainable practices for the sake of survival.

Through diversification and the use of modern technologies, some developing countries have begun to improve the environmental quality of their agriculture. Even so, a massive force over which they still have little leverage—namely, the developed world—often blocks their moves toward sustainability. Between 1980 and 1987, already poor North-South relations worsened. As calculated by colloquium participant Maria de Lourdes Davies de Freitas, a Brazilian government environmental official, the prices of 33 commodities the World Bank monitors fell by 40 percent, costing developing countries perhaps $100 billion a year in lost sales and depressed earnings. In agricultural trade, protectionism and high domestic farm prices within OECD nations take the lead in shaping what the agricultural economist G. Edward Schuh, a colloquium participant, termed a highly distorted sector in which rich countries produce too much food, poor countries produce too little, and the environment suffers everywhere.

The generous subsidies that rich nations often apply to their own farmers—which in the wealthiest countries amount to some $300 billion a year, or six times what they provide in official aid to developing countries—lie at the heart of the problem.[14] Incentives associated with feedlot cattle raising programs in the EC created a vast artificial European market for cassava (manioc) from Thailand. At least 60 percent of the Thai land used to grow cassava was once tropical forest. Grown as it usually is in Thailand—as a monoculture by relatively small farmers—the crop tends to deplete the soil's nutrient supplies and degrade its structure. The spread of profitable cassava cultivation, moreover, has displaced subsistence farmers onto land deep in the forest, or onto steep hillsides. These trends have brought the usual environmental consequences: soil erosion, watershed disruption, and microclimatic change. The same incentive caused the conversion of much fertile cropland in southern Brazil, previously used to grow foodstuffs for domestic consumption, to production of soybeans for export to the EC.

Rich nations provoke environmental as well as economic problems in poor ones by declining to buy what they offer. The best example of this problem is the cane sugar trade. Because of tightening quotas imposed to protect domestic producers, U.S. sugar imports from the Caribbean Basin dropped from an average of 1.66 million tons a year in 1975–1981 to 442,200 tons in 1989,[15] or by 73 percent. Despite high U.S. prices, the net loss to the region was $312 million in 1989. While the U.S.–sponsored Caribbean Basin Initiative has added some 136,000 manufacturing jobs between 1983 and 1988, the decline in quotas cost the region 400,000 jobs over the same period. EC sugar policy, which has transformed Western Europe into a subsidized net exporter and flooded the global market, compounds the problem for all developing country producers, except for ex-colonies whose output receives preferential treatment under the Lomé Convention. In part also because soft drink producers have switched to high-fructose corn syrup, a product that is economically competitive in the United States only because of artificially high prices for cane sugar, global demand for cane sugar has dropped 25 percent from its peak despite the world's rising population.

While governments and corporations in developed countries may see clear political or economic logic in these actions, the effects of such measures on poor producing nations are undeniably negative. Unable to sell their sugar, some Caribbean islands have switched to export crops that do greater environmental damage, such as bananas. More frequently, they have been able to find no alternative to sugar's dominance in their agricultural economies, and the result has been spreading poverty. Late in the 1980s, as a direct consequence of sugar policies that are controlled in developed countries, the hard-pressed Dominican Republic's efficient sugar industry reduced production by 40 percent. Its U.S. quota had been drastically lowered, and producers could not compete internationally, where prices during the 1980s remained no more than half of those that prevail in the protected U.S. market. Efforts to generate equivalent returns from nontraditional crops proved unsuccessful and, in some instances, environmentally harmful. In current dollars per capita gross national product (GNP) sank to two-thirds its 1980 level. Many farm workers left the country: late in the 1980s the Dominican Republic became the world's top supplier of emigrants to the New York City area.

Environmental and economic difficulties arise not only from what developed countries choose to buy from the South, but also from what they sell. An EC decision to supply Togo with subsidized meat sabotaged that country's carefully designed program to encourage the raising of small ruminants. Unloading excess production of rice and other basic commodities at low prices undermines local efforts to achieve balanced rural development. "The dumping from the European Community and the United States makes global prices even lower than they would otherwise be," noted Edward Schuh at the colloquium. "Developing countries become net importers of what they could be producing for themselves, and because of the cheap imports, they do not need to make more rational policy at home. And the fact that they continue to import means that it remains easier for developed countries to continue to practice their predatory or dumping policies. They've developed a symbiotic relationship that is very difficult to change."

The North has long set the rules about matters affecting 85 percent of the world's total volume of $4 trillion or more in annual international trade. Traditionally, developing countries have had little influence at discussions of parties to the General Agreement on Tariffs and Trade (GATT). Although 102 nations had "acceded to" the GATT by mid-1991, its discussions have long centered not on how developing countries could achieve greater access to the international economy or more favorable prices, but on how rich countries could sell more to them.

Moreover, environmental considerations have rarely affected the GATT decision-making process. The trade in tropical timber products, a principal reason why the global rate of tropical deforestation doubled during the 1980s from already unsustainable levels, provides an example. The International Tropical Timber Organization (ITTO), which loosely regulates this trade, maintains as one of its goals the achievement of sustainable tropical forest management. Most of the 44 nations that are ITTO members, and have signed an agreement pledging to develop domestic policies toward this end, are also members of the GATT. Yet in making this commitment, according to a World Wildlife Fund paper presented at the ITTO meeting in Yokohama on November 1991, they risk provoking challenges that are valid under the GATT:

> An established principle of the GATT is that trade restrictions cannot be used to discriminate between "like products" on the basis of the method of production. This means that signatories to the GATT cannot use trade tariffs, quotas or bans to favour trade in sustainably rather than unsustainably-produced tropical timber. Yet the ITTO objective . . . will not be achieved unless trade measures which do precisely this are implemented.[16]

At the Yokohama meeting, the World Wildlife Fund proposed that the ITTO request from the GATT a waiver from regulations interfering with the organization's quest for tropical forestry sustainability, and remind member-countries of their sovereignty with regard to forest resources. If conflict between environmental goals and trade liberalization objectives under the GATT is to be avoided, it will often be necessary to seek these sorts of exceptions.

During the course of the GATT's Uruguay Round, which began in Punta del Este in 1986 and was continuing as of May 1991, the South has achieved greater negotiating power as a result of the increasing role it is playing in world trade. As strapped as they are, developing countries manage to buy about 40 percent of all U.S. exports, and the figure could climb to 50 percent if their economic health increases. For the U.S. economy, these markets are of critical importance if exports (our most important product, analyst Paula Stern has called them) are to expand as rapidly as possible during the 1990s. The Uruguay Round has made it increasingly evident that advanced trading nations will gain even greater access to the South's rapidly expanding high-technology and service-sector markets only if they, in return, offer freer terms of trade in food and textiles over the objections of strongly protectionist domestic lobbies. Complaints from the North that cut-rate pirate producers violate its "intellectual property rights," across a spectrum of products from pills to audiocassettes, have met with counterarguments from developing countries that their genetic resources—the intellectual property of native peoples in poor countries—receive insufficient respect and compensation.

With particular emphasis on agricultural trade, during the Uruguay Round the United States has pressed hard for liberalization. Backed by the Cairns group of fourteen agriculture exporting countries, the United States originally—perhaps with unrealistic enthusiasm—called for the removal of all forms of farm support within ten years. Later, unyielding Western European opposition moved the United States to modify its proposal to a 90 percent reduction in export subsidies and a 75 percent cut in domestic price supports. The EC, home to ten million farmers (vs. two million in the United States), stalled for months, then countered the U.S. position with a suggestion that internal support mechanisms be cut 30 percent with little mention of reductions in export subsidies or easing import restrictions. Other proposed liberalization measures that have emerged during the Uruguay Round include the following:

- Less protection for processing industries in the North, particularly in the agribusiness, minerals, and wood sectors

- Less dumping of farm surpluses in the developing world

- More market access for manufactures from developing countries, to lessen the degree of their dependence on export crops

As of mid-1991 the Uruguay Round faced an uncertain future. Its extension, for perhaps two years, would give negotiators a further chance to work out these differences. But without the fast-track procedure that would require the U.S. Congress to vote "up or down" on trade packages without amending them, domestic lobbyists for special interests (e.g., textiles and a variety of farm products) were likely to prevent the passage of a new program that would be acceptable to other members of the GATT. Congress gave the Uruguay Round a new lease on life through its votes in May 1991 sanctioning the use of the fast track in negotiating the hotly debated U.S.–Mexico free trade agreement as well as the Round itself. Moreover, those interested in liberalization will also have opportunities to pursue this goal through regional trade agreements.

For growers of export crops in developing countries, the movement toward freer trade could bring major economic benefits from the higher world market prices that, according to the economist Ernst Lutz of the World Bank's Environmental Policy and Research Division, would result from liberalization. Opinions vary, however, as to the environmental consequences of such a shift. Optimists believe that several factors—improved returns from the best lands, more international market access for manufactured as well as farm goods from developing countries, technical assistance from rich countries—could combine to spare steep hillsides and tropical forests and sop up available manpower supplies. Others doubt that such fortuitous synergy would be the result. Lutz argues that high unemployment rates in many developing countries and high population growth rates would nullify the "offsetting effect" (as Schuh has termed it), and concludes that the net environmental result would be negative.

Environmentalists harbor other apprehensions about the consequences of the move toward trade liberalization under the GATT. The search for the "harmonization" of environmental rules that could facilitate trade could also compel many countries to accept international rules on food safety, pesticides, or insecticides that are far less stringent than their own national standards. The United Nations–administered Codex Alimentarius, for example, accepts considerably higher concentrations of DDT and other dangerous chemicals than U.S. regulations allow. The international ban on trade in ivory and other products derived from endangered wildlife, which most environmental groups enthusiastically support, is subject to challenge under GATT rules. So are unilateral import bans imposed for environmental reasons that can be interpreted as protection for domestic industries.

While the existing system causes both environmental and economic problems for developing countries, improvement on one side does not automatically lead to improvement on the other. Tighter environmental controls do not necessarily make developing countries more competitive in international markets. "Dirty" imports could do as much environmental harm in developing countries as the export programs that enable them to buy goods from abroad. Trade liberalization and improved environmental quality will become compatible goals only if careful management is applied. Mindful of such uncertainties, colloquium participants were nonetheless able to suggest a number of modifications in the existing system that would ease the path toward concurrent achievement of both these desirable objectives:

- Elaborate and place in force an environmental code. The GATT itself would be the best administrator for such a code. "Hazardous substances and wastes represent a trade issue," Edward Schuh commented at the colloquium. "There's lots of attention to it, but not much interest in moving it along. What we really need is an environmental code, parallel to the disciplines and codes that we have in the GATT trading system, to prescribe what countries can and cannot do in relation to this form of dumping."

- Establish environmental labeling programs, already in increasing use for consumer products in developed countries, to reduce the likelihood of "dirty" imports becoming counterweights to domestic environmental progress in the Third World.

- Implement targeted feeding programs, and a longer-term swing away from exports and toward domestic food production in countries where this is feasible, to alleviate currency devaluations. Often part of adjustment agreements, currency devaluations bring higher prices for imported food and can lead to urban riots.

- Strengthen many international institutions to achieve environmentally beneficial trade reforms. Regardless of other forces having a powerful effect on current trade patterns, such as regional free trade agreements, the GATT will remain the basic vehicle. If it is to be an effective agent for reform, the GATT will have to do a better job of representing its entire constituency.

- Intensify industrial nations' commitment to recycling efforts as a means of reducing their dependence on fresh supplies of raw materials. This is one of many routes to improving the environmental quality of global commerce that lie beyond the GATT.

- Make structural adjustments within OECD nations, particularly in the agricultural sector. Objectives would include overall decreases in agricultural protectionism and in subsidized exports of farm surpluses. Paying off small numbers of domestic workers in obsolete industries is often far more cost-effective, and helpful to consumers, than doomed efforts to make them competitive.

- Develop alternative mechanisms to achieve sustainability in tropical forestry since neither the Tropical Forest Action Plan nor the ITTO has been effective. One possibility is the creation of a North-South arrangement to compensate countries willing to forgo excessive exploitation of tropical forest resources. A global permitting scheme, similar to carbon tax proposals now under discussion as a means of controlling atmospheric pollution, may be feasible.

PUBLIC INVESTMENT

In current dollars the United States would have to be spending some $350 billion a year, or more than 3 percent of GNP, to match what it invested in West European recovery for three straight years following World War II. But in 1989 the entire U.S. program of bilateral and multilateral official development assistance (ODA) represented only 0.15 percent of GNP. The same year only some 15 percent of the total $14 billion U.S. budget for bilateral foreign aid, which includes security assistance, went to support for Third World development. Collectively, the members of the OECD's Development Assistance Committee could muster no more than $46.7 billion in bilateral and multilateral ODA in 1989. This figure represents 0.33 percent of GNP, or one-third of the 1 percent mark that Robert McNamara, while president of the World Bank, earnestly tried to achieve during the 1970s.

In view of the developing countries' debt and trade problems, such sums are far from adequate if these nations are to achieve economic growth targets. "In the course of the 1980s," reported the South Commission, an unofficial forum of prominent individuals from 27 developing countries that convened late in the 1980s, "the international processes of development co-operation that had begun to take shape in earlier decades virtually collapsed."[17] While Third World growth rates remained generally high during the first three postwar development decades, and substantial advances occurred in health and education, the world's poverty rate—the proportion of the total population living in absolute poverty, defined as lacking sufficient income to meet the most basic needs for food, clothing, and shelter—improved only slightly. Record numbers of people in the South fell into this category, and the gap between their living standards and those of OECD nations was widening even before the development crisis of the 1980s worsened the situation in many respects.

During the early post–World War II years the newly created development agencies, dominated then as now by economists and engineers, tended to believe that growth was most likely to occur from comprehensive planning supported by capital-intensive investments in large infrastructure projects and industrial installations. A series of subsequent vogues—first favoring export promotion, then addressing basic needs, then the structural adjustment programs of the 1980s—succeeded this initial preference for import substitution. Common to all four of these principal phases of the development era was a general disregard for the environmental consequences of the recommended actions.

These consequences have been considerable. Large new dams that created electric power and opened new lands for cultivation also destroyed forests, spread waterborne diseases, caused siltation, and forced large numbers of indigenous people to abandon their homes. Development planners measured tropical forests in terms of board feet rather than biological diversity content, and saw the use of farm chemicals mainly as a way to increase yields. Tropical deforestation to make way for cattle pastures, generally the least efficient usage of the rain forest,[18] to this day has its devoted advocates in development circles. The high discount rates the development agencies customarily use for cost-benefit analyses mean that environmental losses carry almost no weight. Were the calculations to include environmental costs as a factor in GNP growth, colloquium participant Robert Repetto of the World

Resources Institute has contended, the new results would sharply weaken the economic records of many developing countries.[19]

Step by step, over the past two decades, aid donors have recognized these deficiencies, and ratcheted up their efforts to incorporate environmental considerations into their planning and funding systems. The World Bank, which appointed its first environmental advisor in 1970, has since issued numerous environmental policy statements, founded its Environment Department (in 1987), and established mandatory environmental assessment procedures that govern most forms of its lending. With varying levels of enthusiasm, all other multilateral aid agencies have followed suit. Among bilateral donors, USAID, under frequent pressure from the U.S. Congress since the mid-1970s to improve its environmental record, has become an environmental leader in the field.

Traditional thinking, however, continues to prevail in many quarters of the development community. As colloquium participant Robert Blake, representing the Committee for Sustainable Agriculture, put it: "The development agencies still have not really tried on sustainable growth even though they have the potential, the resources, and the leadership to help developing countries come to grips with the fact that we need to figure out how to feed 40 percent more people within two decades—with a shrinking base of arable land." Joseph Wheeler seconded Blake's suggestion that part of the problem is an "antirural bias," among aid donors as well as in the capitals of the South. In his five years as chairman of the OECD's Development Assistance Committee, Wheeler noted, he could not recall a single meeting devoted exclusively to agriculture.

A large part of the problem, several colloquium participants felt, is a widespread loss of faith in the development idea. "There's a general perception that development assistance has not been successful," observed Robert Repetto. Hassan Ali Mehran, economic advisor to the government of Aruba, voiced his regret at the weakening of the lively prodevelopment constituency that existed in many rich nations during the 1950s and 1960s. Participants generally agreed that the focus of international politics would shift from East-West to North-South issues in the aftermath of the Persian Gulf war, and that concerns about equity for poor nations would likely increase. But they also felt that the United States, at least, regards support for Third World development as more an act of philanthropy than a sound investment from which to expect a return. "We need to demonstrate that a dollar spent on multilateral programs is cost-effective in terms of achieving U.S. objectives, that it is in the self-interest of the U.S. to strive for a stable political and economic world, address the problems of the global environment, of our fast-growing population," said Michael Gucovsky of the United Nations Development Programme (UNDP). "I'm convinced that the facts support this." The critical need, added James Gustave Speth, president of the World Resources Institute, is to focus public attention away from the perhaps threatening issue of Third World development, and "talk to people in terms of environmental cooperation, of alleviating poverty and doing something about 40,000 children and hundreds of species being lost each day, of land being reduced in terms of productive capacity. With ideas like this you can really communicate."

Sharon Camp of the Population Crisis Committee agreed. "There's a real well of public support for the U.S. helping to solve world problems," she commented. "Our people want to stabilize the population, save children, and preserve the environment. What we must do is set measurable goals about these matters, get a narrow focus on the world problems that we want to solve, and then go out and press home the importance of those issues."

The stage would thus be well set, members of the group concluded, for implementing their many suggestions for improving both the quantity and the environmental quality of ODA flows. These include the following:

- Renew emphasis on developing improved technologies for the rural sector in such areas as plant genetics, soil and water management, and optimum use of farm chemicals.

- Improve rural service institutions.

- Enhance the quality of rural infrastructures—irrigation, off-farm erosion, and flood control mechanisms, watershed management programs, and roads and marketing systems.

- Combat the urban bias with new pricing and land-tenure regimes.

- Increase support for agricultural research centers.

- Return to support for production agriculture as opposed to processing or other "business" aspects of raising crops at both the World Bank and USAID.

- Construct ways for nongovernmental agencies and donor-country companies to use development assistance funds for ecosystem restoration projects, many of which would involve partnerships with host-country governments.

- Hold "town meetings" in the United States and other donor countries in an effort to develop a closer understanding of what forms of aid to Third World nations are most attractive to the taxpayers who underwrite them.

PRIVATE INVESTMENT

The greening of corporate behavior was a significant phenomenon of the 1980s. Increasingly, large corporations found themselves beset by environmentalists, government regulators, Wall Street fund managers, consumers with deepening environmental awareness, and even their own employees. They also suffered from Bhopal, oil spills, and other well-publicized specific setbacks. Not only did they react to these developments; they began to anticipate problems. While hardly blameless in other environmental respects, Du Pont and other corporations exercised creative leadership in helping to bring about the 1987 Montreal Protocol, the initial chapter in the world's effort to reduce usage of the chlorofluorocarbons (CFCs) that damage the atmosphere's ozone layer. In London in 1990, 92 nations—including a reluctant United States—took the dramatic step of agreeing on a timetable for the termination of all CFC usage. Concluding the 1987 agreement, and the subsequent modifications that tightened it, would have been difficult if not impossible if signatory governments had not had the cooperation of the large corporations that have manufactured the widely used product.

"Total quality management" became a familiar phrase among large industrial companies. In 1991 the International Chamber of Commerce convened its second World

Industry Conference on Environmental Management (WICEM II), with the objective of deciding upon "substantive actions and initiatives that indicate both world business' responsibilities and commitment to action toward improved environmental performance and sustainable development."[20] Maurice Strong, the Canadian businessman who served as secretary-general for the 1972 Stockholm Conference on the Human Environment and has assumed the same responsibility for the upcoming UNCED, is impressed. "There's been a tremendous increase in the number of business people who are taking a longer view," he has said.

Less evident is the degree to which this generally more circumspect approach applies to the multinationals' operations and investments in developing countries. Many of them claim that they maintain the same environmental standards for all the countries where they operate. Scott Paper in Indonesia and Coca-Cola in Belize are among the large corporations that have backed off from proposed investments when environmental problems cropped up. In Thailand, Uniroyal Chemical dropped a promising deal when its local partner refused to commit to the U.S. company's environmental standards. Yet in the Third World's least developed areas, the projects that the companies favor are typically in the agribusiness, mining, forestry, or oil sectors—precisely those where the potential for damage to the environment or to indigenous peoples reaches its maximum even if the best and most sensitive technologies are applied. Here as well, regulatory controls are often looser in practice than on paper because of the investment's importance to recipient countries. In the rural Third World, nonprofit environmental monitoring is in shorter supply than in the OECD nations.

Restoring private capital flows to developing countries is, according to colloquium participant William Nitze of the Alliance to Save Energy, the "magic bullet" that can hit the bull's-eye of sustainable growth for developing countries. The combination of the capital, jobs, technology, and infrastructure that industry can provide, he believes, is the economic package most capable of moving poor countries away from poverty-related environmental degradation—without imposing on them the environmental damage that came with industrialization in earlier times. For those concerned with environmental quality the trick is twofold: how to lure these private investors back to the Third World, and how to keep them green—even if no one is watching very carefully.

What will attract private capital to the contemporary Third World? In older times, many statist Southern nations took antagonistic positions that prompted the retreat of the private sector. Now that free market ideas are once again gaining currency in developing countries, leniency toward foreign private investors is waxing. Concessions are granted with regard to proportions of ownership, rules regarding profit remittances, and the extent to which international technologies are allowed to prevail over local competition. How willing developing countries will be to adjust "the rules of the game" remains important. Now as ever, if investors dislike the deal available in one poor country, they are free to proceed to the next.

Changes in industrial nations' economic policies can also expedite the flow of private capital to poor countries. The report of an international conference on the economics of sustainable development sponsored by the Environmental Protection Agency and held in Washington on January 23–26, 1990, stressed that fiscal balance in the

United States would reduce American demand for international capital, and lower real borrowing costs. Vast resources would then, at least in principle, become available for investment in developing countries. Not even such broad modifications in both North and South, however, provide assurance that future private investments in developing countries will be squeaky-green.

Several private groups have attempted to set global environmental standards for private foreign investors. In 1989 the U.S.–based Coalition for Environmentally Responsible Economies (CERES)—with a membership made up of pension funds, church groups, and other nonprofits— assembled a ten-point set of guidelines. The CERES criteria, known as the Valdez Principles, have advocates at shareholders' meetings in the United States and are gaining international currency.

Corporations, more comfortable if they establish their own criteria than if they come under pressure to respond to rules made by others, have swung into action as well. The U.S. Chemical Manufacturers Association has drawn up its own set of "responsible care" principles. Companies must pledge adherence to them to qualify for association membership. The American Petroleum Institute and the International Chamber of Commerce have similar projects under way. Also involved is the Global Environmental Management Initiative (GEMI), a godchild of 21 large U.S.– based corporations whose purpose is to gather and disseminate information on environmental management. While GEMI remains vague about how it will relate to developing countries, it pledges a "worldwide" program to enhance the environmental performance of business, improve environmental management, and encourage sustainable development. Though still small, with a 1990–

1991 budget of $675,000, GEMI's very existence mani-
fests a new stirring in large corporate boardrooms. In
Europe the multinational Business Committee for Sustainable Development began operations in 1991. Canada,
Germany, and Japan are among the countries that now
have environmental business associations.

Some who question whether self-policing mechanisms
will "control" the private sector seek at least a partial
solution in the form of public-private partnerships. One
model for possible replication is the 1987 Montreal Protocol. "When industry accepted the idea of the Montreal
Protocol," said William Nitze at the colloquium, "it actually
did a lot of the planning for the CFC phase-out, and for the
development of substitutes, in conjunction with the U.S.
government. The same kind of thing could happen with
regard to toxic chemicals—not just their registration, but
programs for licensing, storing, and handling them. And I
can see the same principles being applied to the tech-
niques of integrated pest management, though high returns would have to be allowed because the payout would
occur only over the long term."[21]

Other forms of partnership between corporations and
governments or aid agencies offer similar potential, particularly in the important field of technology transfer.
Already, several models are at work. In India USAID
supports the Program for the Acceleration of Commercial
Energy Research, an effort to increase energy efficiency by
making new technologies available to local enterprise. A
similar model, reported colloquium participant Walter
Arensberg of the World Resources Institute, is Fundación
Chile (FCh), a mixed-enterprise corporation whose purpose is to facilitate Chilean access to advanced nations'
technical know-how. FCh was established in 1976, as a

means of resolving a $50 million difference of opinion between the ITT Corporation and the Pinochet regime as to the value of ITT properties that Pinochet's predecessor, Salvador Allende, had expropriated. To avoid a stalemate, the company and the government eventually agreed to split the difference and each invest $25 million in a mutually beneficial activity. During its lifetime FCh has not only substantially increased its own net worth, but also has heightened the level of national technology in a diversity of fields ranging from farming to fisheries to light manufacturing. In a controversial but important move the World Health Organization provided financial support to Roussel Uclaf, a French drug company, to undertake clinical trials of RU-486, the so-called abortion pill. In return, the manufacturer agreed to market the drug in developing countries at an affordable price.

Colloquium participants suggested a variety of new ways in which the public and private sectors might join forces. For example, Robert Repetto recommended "special attention to commercially feasible investments that promote sustainable development" on the part of the World Bank's International Finance Corporation and the U.S. government's Overseas Private Investment Corporation (OPIC). OPIC, which provides political-risk and other forms of insurance as well as loans to U.S. corporations investing in the developing world, claims to follow "World Bank rules" on environmental quality. Such a statement, on the part of this profit-making government corporation, is not wholly reassuring. Even less so is one OPIC official's admission that its two-person environmental staff's monitoring tends toward "the passive side of active." For OPIC to carry out the mandate suggested, in other words, internal adjustments are required.

The World Bank's new Global Environment Facility (GEF) offers ample opportunity for private participation, said Michael Gucovsky, one of its creators. This experimental mechanism for funding sustainable development was established in 1990, under the supervision of the Bank, with UNDP and the United Nations Environment Programme (UNEP) as its partners. Sponsors expect the Facility's initial subscription, of over $1 billion in capital from 25 developed and developing countries, to increase substantially. Within GEF is broad latitude for corporations to seek concessional funding for investment projects in a range of fields from forest management to making the transition from CFCs to other gases that are less harmful to the atmosphere.

At the colloquium Joan Martin-Brown of UNEP suggested that on a competitive basis, private corporations as well as nongovernmental organizations solicit development assistance funds for reforestation projects and other efforts to restore degraded ecosystems. "We need to throw away a lot of the old assumptions," she said. "One thing that must be stopped is the isolation of private from public funds."

One should not ignore the potential of old-fashioned incentives, warned colloquium participant S. Bruce Smart of the World Resources Institute. As an example, he mentioned a Brazilian program in which pulp and paper companies received tax breaks for reforestation, as well as the ownership of the trees they planted. Many foreign companies took advantage of the program. In so doing, they received an environmentally beneficial "kickback" in the sense that the cost of planting trees was less than the tax that would otherwise have been due. Other suggestions that came from colloquium participants were these:

- Implement local import and investment regulations that favor appropriate technologies regardless of their source. In many countries, for example, local manufacturers of standard light bulbs continue to receive favorable treatment even though bulbs having greater energy efficiency could be imported or made locally.

- Recognize excessive bureaucracy and red tape as still a major deterrent to private foreign investment.

- Empower women. They play a prominent role in rural economies, particularly in Asia and Africa. Public agencies, noted Joan Martin-Brown, have already demonstrated what can be done "to create a sustainable rural renaissance" by gathering women into new institutions such as food production cooperatives. Private investors can benefit from the results of entrepreneurship training for women in the rural Third World.

TOWARD UNCED AND BEYOND

The upcoming Earth Summit, as colloquium participant and UNCED staff member Joseph Wheeler describes it, has a variety of functions. It is at once an international education process—something around which to organize public opinion—and a deadline for completing negotiations now in progress. It is, moreover, a means of correcting an oversight of the 1972 Stockholm Conference by incorporating development into the environmental idea— and a broad opportunity to set an agenda and new global goals for the coming century.

Environmental experts and growing numbers of lay

leaders have long been outlining the sweeping "global bargain" between developed and developing nations that could emerge from the UNCED process and subsequent negotiations. Developing countries would pledge to address the population question with new determination, and sharply curtail deforestation and other environmentally destructive practices. In return for a broad commitment from the South, Northern nations would reduce atmospheric pollution so that overall greenhouse stability might be achieved even as developing countries increase their emissions enough to advance their growth rates. Controls on greenhouse gas emissions, a matter already under intense international scrutiny, would represent only part of the Northern commitment. Greater equity would also result from the new forms of Northern assistance to alleviate Southern distress on the debt, trade, and investment issues that this report mentions. Grappling with these gigantic tasks may require new institutions or a broad revamping of existing ones.

Daunting in the opinion of some observers, the dimensions of the contemplated adjustment are small in comparison with the world's military budgets. As of 1990 the world was still spending about $1 trillion a year—almost as much as the putative value of the developing world's entire debt—on armaments. A 10 percent cut in NATO's military spending, the World Bank has pointed out, is equivalent to a doubling of all foreign aid.[22] For 15 percent of all military outlays, or roughly $150 billion a year during the latter 1990s, the world could take the steps required to achieve sustainable development by the year 2000 in such categories as preventing soil erosion, reforestation, increasing energy efficiency, and addressing the population question.[23] Actions such as U.S. Defense

Secretary Dick Cheney's early 1991 decision to cancel the $57 billion A-12 attack aircraft, after only $1.2 billion had been spent, would carry the world far toward the goal. Though the Gulf war prolonged indefinitely the time when deep U.S. cuts in high-tech tactical weapons will be politically negotiable, countless billions could be free for other purposes if the United States and the Soviet Union were to consummate the reductions in strategic arms that were posited after the June 1990 summit meeting. Ideas abound about how not to disband the conventional military apparatus in the United States, but to convert it to other purposes.

Not everyone believes that progress toward sustainability can be bought so cheaply or easily. But even if the price tag becomes larger, simply passing some of the cost on to consumers will lessen it. Much of the total public investment required could, moreover, come through reprogramming of what is already budgeted or forecast. Tens of billions of foreign aid dollars now going to purposes other than development assistance can be reallocated in support of sustainability. Some people have even begun to think that good ideas are in shorter supply than the funds to implement them.

The North has many basic political reasons for wanting to pay an affordable price for global sustainability. Environmentally as well as economically, the relationship between Northern interests and a healthy South draws ever closer. With natural resources looming as the probable cause of many regional conflicts in the future, and with nuclear proliferation making inexorable progress from land to land, local environmental wars could pose grave threats to all people. Use of the environment itself as a tool of war, an old practice that Saddam Hussein extended from the battlefield to the ecosystem level, will remain an ever more lethal threat. The South, with its fast-growing population, holds great potential as a market for Northern exports—if it can afford to pay for the goods it will want to buy. Ecological distress would, on the other hand, increase the flow of environmental refugees from Asia, Africa, and many parts of the Western Hemisphere into nations of the developed world that find it difficult to provide adequate services for their existing populations.

For all the appeal of these sorts of arguments, the depth of the North's commitment to environmental health in the rural Third World remains questionable. Although many economists and others find good reason to incorporate economic and environmental factors into the "security equation," the term is still often defined strictly in terms of military power. In the United States the underlying basis of foreign economic policy in the 1990s has little to do with the needs of the poor in developing countries, let alone the quality of their environments. "Competitiveness" is the broad term that dominates the economic "vision" at the White House, which is weary of not having a "level playing field" for global commerce. Even within the development assistance portion of the foreign aid budget, U.S. export considerations loom far larger than sustainability. These realities support the notion, stressed at the colloquium, that development assistance for the Third World can gain support in the United States only if it is dramatically repackaged for broader appeal to the electorate.

Sharply differing perceptions about what comes first also remain between North and South. Edward Seaga, the former prime minister of Jamaica, who while in office symbolized economic orthodoxy and submitted his struggling country to adjustment assistance without a human face, put it well in his opening remarks at the colloquium. "The drumbeats of the North," he warned, "do not automatically translate into rhythms in the South, even where there is conviction and willingness and the means are provided." His conclusion:

> Too much of the programming and formulation of policies to deal with complex global issues tends to reflect macro views without sufficiently considering the microcosm of society, the household, and its perceptions of the problems and solutions as seen through the demands of the kitchen economy. Any Third World agenda on environmental issues will place shelter, fuel, water, and energy at the top of the list. Likewise, deforestation in the mind-set of environmentalists everywhere is a major issue, contributing as it does to the feared greenhouse effect of atmospheric warming, depletion of water resources, and the massive loss of topsoil through soil erosion.
>
> The industrial world, accomplished as it is in putting men on the moon, orbiting the earth, telecommunicating from one end of the world to the other, building tunnels under the sea, harnessing nuclear power, biogenetically creating new life forms, and creating computers with awesome capacity, cannot be held to be seriously concerned about the environment if in this advanced technological age it still cannot light a poor man's home atop a distant hill, or allow him to cook his meals without denuding his own landscape.

Beyond priorities lie fundamental questions about how people approach life. In negotiating the global bargain, Northerners may find it hard to adjust their thinking to sharply contrasting ideas about space, time, and distance that still prevail in the villages of the Third World. For all the blinding speed of modern communications, perceptions about money, values, and cadences continue to differ. During the 1970s the world debated the so-called new international economic order, which, with little reference to environmental issues, would have involved major financial transfers from North to South to bring about greater global harmony. But the North proved unwilling to loosen its purse strings, the talks failed, and the developing world was condemned to the reversals of the 1980s. Now again, as many of its leaders make amply clear, the South expects a payoff in return for environmental pledges. But even with more at stake, the North seems little readier than it was two decades ago to pump large amounts of unrestricted cash into Southern coffers.

Over the course of a series of "prepcom" meetings the UNCED secretariat has organized, delegations of government officials and nongovernmental representatives have been struggling to pave the way for a successful outcome in Rio de Janeiro. It is not a simple task. Even at the national level, let alone in the more complex rough-and-tumble of global discourse, observed colloquium participant Joseph Wheeler, it has been difficult to establish good working relationships between the development and the environmental bureaucracies, or to incorporate the thinking of nongovernmental agencies and business organizations wanting to express views. A principal challenge for UNCED is to include a broad diversity of opinions, yet also keep the process manageable. "To try to agree on 70 to 90 issues by June 1992 is not workable," commented Michael Gucovsky. Added James Gustave Speth: "If UNCED comes up with a catalogue of everybody's wish list, then its results will be inadequate. It would be better to develop a few critical initiatives, and get agreement on them."

If all goes well in Rio de Janeiro, the world will at least have reached broad agreement on how to approach such critical issues as global climate change, biological diversity, and forest usage. Participants will have set forth an

"Earth Charter" and an "Agenda 21" to act as guides to multilateral management of the planet. They will have mapped out scenarios for subsequent global and regional dialogue. Many nations will emerge with greater determination to take unilateral actions. The importance of achieving these objectives is considerable, for the failure of this Green Round would consign the world to a future during which—increasingly for environmental reasons— the walls between the planet's usually urban rich and its rural poor would grow ever higher and less surmountable. The costs of redressing the imbalances, and the dangers involved, will surely rise as the world's population increases and pressures on the environment become more intense. For those in OECD nations who seek to help avoid these dangers by taking preemptive actions now, a sound place to begin is with the agenda outlined here.

NOTES

1. Robert Repetto made this forecast in his monograph "Population, Resources, and Environment: An Uncertain Future," *Population Bulletin*, vol. 42, no. 2 (1987). Repetto is far less optimistic than the World Bank, which anticipates an overall *reduction* in world poverty by 2000 if economic growth in developing countries accelerates and other conditions remain favorable. See World Bank, *World Development Report 1990* (New York: Oxford University Press, 1991). Estimates of the current numbers of Third World poor come from United Nations Development Programme (UNDP), *Human Development Report 1990* (New York City: Oxford University Press, 1991), p. 85.

2. See Peter H. Raven, "Our Diminishing Tropical Forests," in Edward O. Wilson and Francis M. Peter, eds., *Biodiversity* (Washington, D.C.: National Academy Press, 1988), pp. 119–122.

3. Edward O. Wilson, *Biophilia* (Cambridge, Mass., and London: Cambridge University Press, 1984).

4. Of many definitions of the popular term "sustainability," the one cited most frequently is used in the United Nations World Commission on Environment and Development, *Our Common Future* (New York: Oxford University Press, 1987). That benchmark document referred to sustainability as a process that "meets the needs of the present without compromising our ability to meet those of the future," p. 8.

5. See Jim MacNeill, "Strategies for Sustainable Development," *Scientific American*, September 1989, p. 154–165.

6. See Herman Daly, "Sustainable Growth: An Impossibility Theorem," *Development*, no. 3/4 (1990), pp. 45–46.

7. See World Bank, *World Development Report 1990*, p. 141.

8. UNDP, *Human Development Report 1990*, p. 34, 79; OECD, *Development Assistance Report 1990* (Washington, D.C.: 1990), p. 122–126.

9. UNDP, *Human Development Report 1990*, p. 79.

10. As quoted by Mohamed T. El-Ashry in a speech at the University of Oslo and the Nobel Institution, February 12, 1991.

11. Comparision cited at the colloquium by Alvaro Umaña Quesada.

12. World Bank, *Sub-Saharan Africa: From Crisis to Sustainable Growth* (Washington, D.C., 1989), p. 48.

13. World Bank, *World Development Report 1990*, p. 12.

14. From Jim MacNeill's "Sustainable Development, Economics, and the Growth Imperative." (Paper presented at the U.S. Environmental Protection Agency's Workshop on Economics and Sustainable Development, Washington, D.C., January 23–26, 1990.)

15. Overseas Development Council, "U.S. Sugar Quotas and the Caribbean Basin," *Policy Focus*, no. 6 (1989).

16. Charles Arden-Clarke, "Conservation and Sustainable Management of Tropical Forests: The Role of ITTO and GATT," World Wildlife Fund discussion paper, ITTO meeting, Yokohama, November 16–23, 1990.

17. The South Commission, *The Challenge to the South* (New York: Oxford University Press, 1990).

18. As the ecologist Robert J.A. Goodland of the World Bank has often stressed.

19. In his often-cited analysis of Indonesian development, Repetto concluded that the average Indonesian growth rate of 7 percent between 1971 and 1984 would drop to 4 percent if environmental degradation were factored in. See Robert Repetto and William B. Magrath, *Wasting Assets: Natural Resources in the National Income Accounts* (Washington, D.C.: World Resources Institute, 1989).

20. From brochure announcing WICEM II, held in Rotterdam, April 9–12, 1991; some 750 delegates attended the conference.

21. Integrated pest management systems depend more on biological than on chemical controls, and they do diminish, if not avoid, the use of harmful chemicals.

22. World Bank, *World Development Report 1990*, p. 4.

23. See the Worldwatch Institute, *State of the World 1988* (New York and London, 1988), pp. 170–188.

Appendix:
Colloquium Participants

Walter Arensberg—*World Resources Institute*
Robert O. Blake—*Committee on Agricultural Sustainability for Developing Countries*
Joan Martin-Brown—*United Nations Environment Programme*
Sharon L. Camp—*Population Crisis Committee*
Nomsa Daniels—*Council on Foreign Relations*
Arba Diallo—*United Nations Conference on Environment and Development*
Marc Dourojeanni—*Inter-American Development Bank*
Maria de Lourdes Davies de Freitas—*Instituto Brasiliero do Meio-Ambiente e Recursos Naturais Renováveis*
Michael Gucovsky—*United Nations Development Programme*
Peter Hakim—*Inter-American Dialogue*
Eve Hamilton—*Council on Foreign Relations*
John Maxwell Hamilton—*The World Bank*
William A. Hewitt—*former U.S. Ambassador to Jamaica*
Shafiqul Islam—*Council on Foreign Relations*
Stephen Kass—*Berle, Kass & Case*
Kenneth H. Keller—*Council on Foreign Relations*
John D. Macomber—*Export-Import Bank of the United States*
Hassan Ali Mehran—*Economic Advisor to the Government of Aruba*
Audrey McInerney—*Council on Foreign Relations*
William A. Nitze—*Alliance to Save Energy*
John R. Petty—*Petty-FBW Associates*
Gareth Porter—*Environmental and Energy Study Institute*
Jack Raymond—*JR Consulting Services, Inc.*
Robert Repetto—*World Resources Institute*
Nicholas X. Rizopoulos—*Council on Foreign Relations*
G. Edward Schuh—*Humphrey Institute of Public Affairs, University of Minnesota*

The Rt. Hon. Edward Seaga, P.C., M.P.—*Former Prime Minister, Jamaica*

S. Bruce Smart—*World Resources Institute*

Mark J. Smith—*Council on Foreign Relations*

James Gustave Speth—*World Resources Institute*

Roger D. Stone—*Council on Foreign Relations*

John Temple Swing—*Council on Foreign Relations*

Peter Tarnoff—*Council on Foreign Relations*

Margaret M. Taylor—*Ambassador of Papua New Guinea to the United States*

Eleanor Tejirian—*The American Assembly*

Sarah Timpson—*United Nations Development Programme*

Alvaro Umaña Quesada—*Instituto Centroamericano de Administración y Empresas, Costa Rica*

Joseph C. Wheeler—*Organization for Economic Cooperation and Development*

About the Authors

Roger D. Stone is Consultant on Environmental Issues at the Council on Foreign Relations and Senior Fellow at the World Wildlife Fund—U.S. He has been Whitney H. Shepardson Fellow at the Council on Foreign Relations, a vice president of the World Wildlife Fund, president of the Center for Inter-American Relations, a vice president of the Chase Manhattan Bank, and a foreign correspondent and news bureau chief for *Time* magazine. A frequent writer and commentator on global environmental issues, he is the author of *Dreams of Amazonia* (Elisabeth Sifton Books/Viking, 1986, Penguin Books, 1986) and *The Voyage of the Sanderling* (Alfred A. Knopf, 1990, Vintage Books, 1991). His forthcoming book *The Nature of Development*, which will incorporate some of the material from this publication, will be published by Alfred A. Knopf, in association with the Council on Foreign Relations, early in 1992.

Eve Hamilton is a former research assistant at the Council on Foreign Relations. She is currently Project Coordinator for the *Policy Focus* briefing paper series and the *Washington Economic Watch: A Digest of Development Policy Information*, two publications on U.S.–Third World issues, at the Overseas Development Council.

The Council on Foreign Relations publishes authoritative and timely books on international affairs and American foreign policy. Designed for the interested citizen and specialist alike, the Council's rich assortment of studies covers topics ranging from economics to regional conflict to East-West relations. If you would like more information, please write:

Council on Foreign Relations Press
58 East 68th Street
New York, NY 10021
(212) 734-0400
Fax: (212) 861-1789